The Willow Tree

and other
English folk dances

26 dances & 52 tunes

A collection from Hugh Rippon & Dave Mallinson

Dave Mallinson Publications 1996

Acknowledgments

Thanks are due to Malcolm Taylor of Vaughan Williams Memorial Library at Cecil Sharp House and to Dave Mallinson who did so much work on the tunes. I would also like to mention with gratitude two local bands with whom I have been connected for a very long time, namely, *Magic Rantabout*, since the days of the Village Pump in Coventry and then, a little later, *Peeping Tom*. Unbeknown to them, many of my ideas came while I was working with them.

HR

The Willow Tree

A collection of dances and tunes from Hugh Rippon and Dave Mallinson

All tunes traditional except *Putney Reach* and *Charabanc schottische*, © John Kirkpatrick and used with permission

All other melody arrangements © 1996 Dave Mallinson

Harmony arrangements © 1996 David J Taylor

All ideas contained herein are obviously intended to be put into practice, but please note that where any of the participants of such practice are receiving any form of remuneration, fees may be incurred for the use of such ideas. Contact the publishers for more details.

First produced and published in England 1996 by Dave Mallinson Publications

3 East View, Moorside, Cleckheaton, West Yorkshire, England BD19 6LD

Telephone 01274 876388, *facsimile* 01274 865208, *e-mail* mally@mally.com, *web url* http://www.mally.com

ISBN 1 899512 26 8

British Library Cataloguing in Publication Data

A catalogue record for this book is available from the British Library

Titles set in *Oxford;* text set in *Aldine;* chord names set in *Franklin Gothic;* music engraved in *Interlude;* page layout in *QuarkXPress*

Cover photographs of Hugh Rippon and willow tree by Ron Hill, © Ron Hill 1995 and used with permission

Cover photograph of Dave Mallinson by David J Taylor, © David J Taylor 1996 and used with permission

Cover design by Ledgard Jepson, telephone 01226 766608

Data input by Dave Mallinson and David J Taylor

Typesetting, data manipulation and page design by David J Taylor

Printed by Rap Limited, Rochdale, telephone 01706 44981

Index to dances

Index to tunes

*h*UGH RIPPON was born and bred in Congleton, Cheshire, lived in Huntingdon and Gloucestershire and subsequently went to Peterhouse, Cambridge where he took an honours degree in history in 1955.

He first became interested in folk dance and song in 1957 shortly after moving to London and in 1960 he joined the full time staff of the *English Folk Dance and Song Society.* Here he acted as Public Relations Officer, Joint Editor of the Society's magazine *English Dance and Song* and London Area Organiser. During this period he spent much of his time teaching dancing, lecturing, writing articles and starting new morris sides. After he left he taught history at a further education college in Coventry.

He took early retirement in 1990 and lives in Earlsdon, Coventry with his wife and four children. He maintains a keen interest in folk dance and music, is holder of the coveted EFDSS Gold Badge and has become one of the most respected and sought-after callers in the country.

Besides his 'calling' activities in most parts of England, Hugh has taught English folk dancing in Holland, Belgium, France and America. He is also the author of *Discovering English Folk Dance,* published by Shire Publications, which is now in its third edition.

Foreword

About this collection of dances.

Many of these dances are my own compositions; others I have collected over the years. Recently there has been some argument about 'made-up' dances. In fact all dances have been made up at some time or another. Many have evolved from bright ideas, some even from mistakes by dancers or teachers. It has always struck me that the best made-up dances have sprung out of previously composed dances: very rarely does a creation calculated in cold blood work. Many dances depend on their success only on personal presentation by the creator: they do not work in other hands. Many are merely repetitions or rearrangements of what have gone before. At one time there were some 10,000 English country dances in print. How many of these have survived?

There are four basic essentials of any good English country dance, be it simple or complex. They are, firstly, an introduction to the next couple or couples; secondly, an outstanding feature or characteristic or 'game' element often with some sort of repetition; thirdly, re-establishment of relationship with one's partner and, fourthly, a clearly defined progression. Above all, the dance should have an intrinsic danceable quality rather than being merely a series of military-like manœuvres, although some people seem to prefer the latter.

Presentation of material

Descriptions are as accurate and consistent as possible. Tunes are suggested for all the dances as a guide; you can use these or, if you prefer, pick similar ones. Historical notes and attributions are given as accurately as possible.

Women or ladies, boys or gents

There have been some terrible descriptions in the past, especially for women who have been called all sorts of things from 'gals' to 'honeys'. I have even been ticked off for using the term 'ladies' ("I'm not a lady, I'm a woman", was one memorable occasion.). There have also been great howlers like "Ladies go to the gents" or vice versa. Etymologically a caller can get into deep water.

In the end I went back to John Playford and have used the terms 'man' and 'woman'. In some dances the initiative can be taken by either. I can quite understand why historically the men were supposed to take the initiative and do the leading but I often find in fact that the women have far more idea about what is supposed to be going on than the men.

Glossary of terms

There have been many ways to describe dances and not all of them have been consistent, even within the same publication. I went through them all and came up with the following:

Longways duple proper: A longways dance for as many as will, men on the right (looking from the top of the set), women on the left, in other words their proper side. The term 'duple' is used because couples are numbered ones or twos all the way down the set. The dance is progressive in that the ones work their way down the set and the twos up. Every other turn there will be a spare (or neutral) couple at the top and bottom who wait one turn before moving the other way up or down the set. The dance can start even if there is a spare couple at the bottom of the set - they simply wait until a new couple comes to them.

This dance formation is the most problematic to teach to the uninitiated because many people find it difficult to grasp the idea of progressing and of being 'neutral' or spare every now and then.

Longways duple improper: This is the same as above except that all first couples are on the wrong side (or 'improper'). The twos are on their own (or 'proper') side. Neutral couples must not forget to cross over while they are waiting at the top or bottom of the set to join in the next turn of the dance when it comes to them.

Couples in a circle facing counter-clockwise: This is exactly what it says. The men are always on the inside of the circle. Progression is optional these days and can be done with the man moving to the woman in front.

Sicilian circle: One couple is facing another couple in a large circle. The woman is on the man's right. Half the couples face clockwise, the others counter-clockwise. The progression is in the direction that the couples are facing. This formation was first described in 1822 by G.M.S. Chivers. He called it Circassian but later it came to be known as Sicilian.

Double Sicilian circle: This is exactly the same as the above except that there are two couples in one line facing two couples in another. The formation is sometimes called Double Quadrille.

Big circle: All the dancers form a large circle facing the centre. The woman is on the man's right.

Longways whole set for three couples: These are longways sets of three couples only, men in one line, women in the other, men on the right (looking from the top of the set), women on the left. The progression is to the bottom of the set, hence the term 'whole'. Most of these three couple set dances were at one time done as longways sets of six couples or even more and many of the older duple longways dances were also 'triple' but people got fed up with waiting at the top or bottom of the set for two goes before they joined in again. The first couples had the best of it: they were 'active' all the time but the twos and threes used to get bored, muddled or both.

Longways whole set for four six or eight couples: These are the same as the above except for the number of couples in the set. The progression is to the bottom of the set unless otherwise specified, for example in *The Willow Tree*. The origin of these longways whole set dances is not known. There maybe some significance in the fact that the top couple usually has a 'pride of place' or 'showing off' part to play and that every one has a turn at being 'number one', a challenge almost. The Irish versions often have fifteen couples with five couples at a time being 'active'.

Square set: These are in fact derived from nineteenth century quadrille figures which became extremely fashionable in the ballroom. There are four couples, woman on the man's right, in a square formation. (Sometimes I have to describe this as being 'like a circle with corners'). The first couple have their backs to the band and the others number round counter-clockwise. The 'head' couples are numbers one and three and the 'side' couples are numbers two and four.

4

General advice for beginners

Many people after their first experience of folk dance often want to find out more, for example how to do the dances, how to learn the steps, how to do the figures and what books are available. The answers are that there are indeed printed sources describing these matters. Some have elaborate plans of footwork, others have diagrams of little matchstick people or even photographs. All are useful but probably the best way to learn is through participation and observation of the real thing. If one relies solely on a book one will only end up with a headache. It is far better to attend as many events as possible and to build up experience. New dancers should initially watch out for and master the following main figures:

1 Right and left hand star;
2 Advance and retire in lines;
3 Promenade or gallop down the set with your partner;
4 Grand chain;
5 Figure of eight or hey or reel;
6 Circle left and/or right;
7 Ladies chain;
8 Basket;
9 Balance and swing;
10 Dance around as a couple;
11 Right and left four or through;
12 Strip the willow;
13 Cast out left and right;
14 Dip and dive and
15 All four ladies chain.

There are also many sorts of stepping for example:

1 Hornpipe or schottische, single or double step;
2 Skip change step;
3 Pas de bas step;
4 Rant or polka step;
5 Waltz step;
6 Walking step;
7 Pivot swing step and
8 Skipping step.

The main advice is to start moving with the other dancers with a walking or skipping step and listen to the message that the music is giving. Later on technique can be improved. For example, the timing and phrasing of movements, reacting sociably with the other dancers, poise, when to use free expression or when to be restrained.

Finally it might help to remember that since one has only two feet the permutations of steps are basically limited to single or double step. A good general tip is to keep one's feet fairly close together and under the body. The late Douglas Kennedy, former director of the *English Folk Dance and Song Society* (EFDSS), used to tell the tale of a brainy Professor of Mathematics who at one of his dance sessions insisted on knowing on which foot he should start the dance. Douglas, for the sake of argument, advised the left foot and then watched in horror as the full might of the professor's brain was concentrated on the unfortunate left foot. The result was that on the first note of the music the professor fell over. The story illustrated well his theory that brain power is a relatively recent development and that natural bodily movements are much older and should be more highly prized when it comes to dancing. There is much to be said for this theory.

Advice for teachers

There are many publications of dance notation from the re-edited dances of John Playford and those who followed him, from the Community Dances Manuals published by the EFDSS and from recent publications by modern M.C.s. The main point to remember about all these is that they should be regarded as aide-memoires and in the early days of teaching or learning the first experience of a dance should be the doing of it backed up by the written word, for in that way alone can the characteristics of a dance emerge. Besides the main figures of a dance, teachers and 'callers' should be aware of the following, in this order:

1 The shape of the dance, for example, longways progressive, longways whole set, circle, Sicilian circle, double Sicilian circle, square, or couple dance etc;
2 The type of music needed for the dance, for example, jig (fast or slow), reel, hornpipe (fast or slow); schottische, waltz, slip jig, rant, polka or march;
3 The length of each dance figure, for example, 16 bars (an A and a B), 32 bars (2 x A, 2 x B), 48 bars (2 x A, 2 x B, 2 x C or 2 x A, 2 x B, 1 x A, 1 x C), sometimes 24 bars, sometimes even 40;
4 The number of times a dance is taken through, although this is often optional and
5 Whether the dance is proper or improper, in other words whether the first couple is on their own side or have crossed over.

At the publisher's suggestion I have indicated for each dance the possible steps to be used, although these are of course optional; much depends on the music. Traditional country dancers often used, wherever possible, to perform their own individual steps and I am glad to see this tradition returning among some modern dancers.

After you, sir

Formation: longways, couples facing couples in two long lines, woman on the man's right.

Music: 32 bar hornpipes.

Step: single or double step as appropriate.

A1 Each man on the right-hand side (facing down) of the set circles to the left once only with the two women then hands them over to the other man (on the left-hand side) with the words "after you, sir". This man then circles once to the left with the two women and hands them back to the first man (on the right-hand side); message repeated.

A2 First man takes the two women (one on either side) down the set with the second man following behind. He hands the women over to the second man who brings them back with the first man following behind. Finish in place with the two women standing back-to-back, the men facing them on the outside.

B1 Set to each other to the right and to the left twice (a variety of setting steps is available) and swing each other with a two-hand cross-hand hold finishing with the woman on the man's right, facing the other couple across the set.

B2 Promenade around each other back to place (using a travelling double step), then all couples move one place to the right to face a new couple (progression is thus counter-clockwise). At this point there will be a neutral couple at either end of the set who, while waiting one turn, will move to their right onto the other side ready for the following turn.

I devised this dance in June 1972 and first presented it at Green's Norton, Northamptonshire, England. The inspiration for this dance came from the Scottish dance The Glasgow Highlanders, from which dancers may use the setting step in B1.

The Glenbeigh

The home ruler

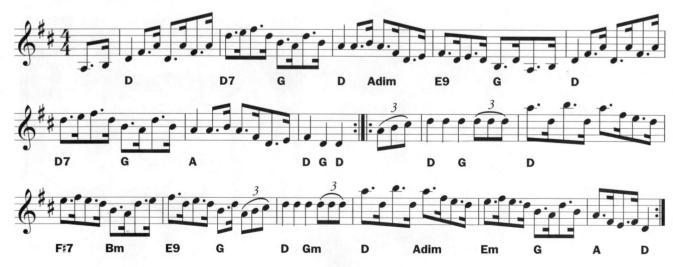

Ap Shenkin

Formation: longways duple proper.

Music: 32 bar single jigs.

Step: skipping or walking step.

A1 First couple form a circle of three with the second woman and circle to the left twice around.

A2 First couple then form a circle of three with the second man and circle to the left twice around.

B1 First couple promenade down the centre with the 'Gay Gordons' or 'Allemande' hold, turn without letting go and promenade home to place (man's left hand held high going down, right hand high coming home). Keep the hold facing the music, the twos join in behind with the same hold.

B2 First couple cast off to the man's left followed by the second couple. Describe a small circle, back to place and then another half-circle to progress, taking care to finish on the proper side.

I learned this dance from a Miss Evans during an EFDSS holiday course in Jersey, Easter 1960. She described it as an American dance of Welsh origin from an unknown manuscript collection but in fact it was first published in Wheatstone Collection of Elegant Country Dances Volume 1 1806-15. This delightfully simple dance is a very good one to teach people the idea of duple progression because they do not lose contact with their partners. Welsh speakers will of course realise that the title 'Ap Shenkin' or 'Ap Siencyn' to be more correct, means Jenkinson.

John of Paris

Ap Shenkin

The Willow Tree

This illustrates the Allemande hold.
The style of music and dress are anachronistic!

'The Country Dance' or 'The Happy Marriage'
W Hogarth, 1753

Around one

Formation: longways whole set for three couples.

Music: 32 bar New England single reels.

Step: walking step.

A1 Lines go forward and back then cross to the other side by the middle couple turning each other with the right hand one-and-a-half times while the end couples do a half-right and left four around them (hence the title).

A2 Repeat the above to original places.

B1 All three couples do a right- and left-hand star.

B2 First couple lead down the middle of the set to the bottom place (progression). The rest of the set moves up a place and all swing

or

if the dance is done as a triple minor longways the first couple lead down the middle and back then cast one place only.

I learned this from William Ganniford at a dance in a very gloomy church hall in Bristol in 1961 or 1962. By the shape of the dance it could well be an older New England triple minor longways dance.

Reel de Ti-Jean

Green Mountain petronella

The Willow Tree

The Aylesbury duck

Formation: longways duple proper.

Music: 32 bar polkas.

Step: walking step.

A1 First man turns second woman with the right hand and then he turns his partner with the left hand a complete turn.

A2 Second man turns the first woman with the right hand and his partner with the left.

B1 First couple lead down the set followed by the second who make an arch for the first couple to duck under (4 bars). All lead back to place then the first couple casts into second place (progression) (4 bars).

B2 Everybody swing.

This dance evolved at one of the Haddenham, Buckinghamshire ceilidhs in 1976 and in fact is merely a variation of The Rose Tree. The follow-down by the second couple and the ducking under are optional since it achieves no real purpose. The Aylesbury Duck is a famous breed of duck.

Grandfather's tune

Clow Bank

The Berkshire fool

Formation: circle facing the centre with the woman on the man's right.

Music: 32 bar single jigs.

Step: walking step.

A1 All go to the centre and back twice.

A2 All face partner. Right hand turn partner all the way round, then left hand turn the person behind all the way round. Repeat. Finish facing partner in the original direction.

B1 Grand chain to five places starting with the right hand but with the fifth person everybody does a back-to-back (do-si-do).

B2 Everybody swing this new partner finishing with the woman on the man's right.

I learned this dance from Pete Gregory at one of the famous Earlsdon ceilidhs at the Hare and Hounds pub, Keresley, Coventry in 1978. He learned it from Brian Jones who had collected it from a Simon Hill, a student at Reading University who supposedly was "not a very good dancer" but nevertheless devised this interesting and ingenious variant on the Lucky Seven. Note how the grand chain starts behind the phrase of music but picks it up again at the end. Moral: never pass value judgements on people's dancing ability.

The perfect cure

Upton upon Severn stick dance

The Willow Tree

The Blue Circle dance

Formation: double Sicilian circle.

Music: 32 bar Irish polkas.

Step: walking step.

A1 All join hands and circle left to original places.

A2 Break the circle into two lots of right- and left-hand stars (each couple with the couple facing them).

B1 Balance and swing partners.

B2 Lines go forward and back and pass on to the next line of couples round the room.

This dance evolved on the spur of the moment in 1970 at a ceilidh during the Bromyard Folk Festival. We were dancing in Mr Morris' shed in which he manufactured concrete blocks and the place was packed with people (and dust). I needed a dance that could be done in such conditions. Would Portland Fancy fit the bill? No, but this instantaneous adaptation might and it did. First, the figures and progression are easy for large numbers of eager but uninitiated dancers. Second, the shape of the dance is flexible (the circle can be done as an oval). Finally, every square inch of space can be used economically. Since we were in a building of concrete connotations and the inspiration was the Portland Fancy. I thought of the title Portland Cement but later changed it to the current one.

An gallope

Sharon Shannon's

Bridgwater Bay

Formation: longways whole set for three couples.

Music: 32 bar innocuous single reels.

Step: walking step.

A1 First couple balance once only to the right and left and cast out one place (second couple move up, first progression). First man makes a three-hand right-hand star with the bottom couple while the first woman does the same with the new top couple.

A2 First couple pass each other by the left shoulder and star left with the other couple. First couple finish in the middle position holding hands in line, men with men, women with women. Balance once to the right and once to the left then, with the men making an arch, all cross to other side and turn to face partners.

B1 Everybody swing, finishing on one's own side but facing the bottom couple, holding inside hands.

B2 Dip and dive, starting with the bottom couple going under the first arch and so on all the way through to original place but the original first couple make one more arch to finish at the bottom of the set (final progression).

This dance, based on a Scottish idea, was composed by myself in April 1972 in honour of Trevor Reynolds' (of Weston-super-Mare, Somerset) twenty-first birthday and subsequently published in English Dance and Song Vol. 4, winter 1973. The dance can move across the phrase of the music and everybody is active most of the time so there is little time for idle chatter.

Maggie May

Little old log cabin

Circle 3 & under the arch OR The Gentle shepherd

Formation: square set for four couples.

Music: 32 bar New England single jigs (see below right).

Step: walking step.

Intro

8 bars Honour your partner, honour your corner.

8 bars All join hands and circle left.

8 bars Swing when you're home.

Figure

4 bars Head gent only lead to the right and circle three. Under the arch and cross the set.

4 bars Circle three and under again.

4 bars Take your lady on to the opposite. Circle four and under again.

4 bars Lady go right and gent go left. Circle three, go under and swing.

8 bars Six go round and round the ring.

Chorus

8 bars Do-si-do your corners all, do-si-do your partners all.

16 bars Allemande left your corners all. Right to your own and chain the ring.

Repeated by second, third and fourth couples in turn

I interpreted this dance off a 78 r.p.m. record in the early sixties while I was working at Cecil Sharp House. This is all I know about the origin. It is obviously American. I give here the original call, which was not exactly a singing call, rather a rhythmic one. The total length of the dance is 48 bars times 4, plus 24 bars for the introduction which is not repeated. The original tune was The Gentle Shepherd. The dance does not last very long and is thus probably a good opener for a longer one to follow.

Eb's dance or Eb's square

Formation: square set for four couples.
Music: 32 bar New England single jigs with an extra 8 bar introduction.
Step: walking step.

Intro
(Once only) honour partners, honour corners.

Figure
A1 First couple only swing.

A2 First couple promenade outside the set and back to place.

B1 First couple do-si-do with second couple (on their right - man round woman and woman round man, passing right shoulders). First couple do the same with fourth couple (on their left).

B2 First couple right and left four with third couple (facing them).

Chorus
A3 All face partner and grand chain all way round the set but half-way round do a do-si-do with partner and

A4 carry on to place. Second time through the dance: couple number two leads, do-si-do-ing with couples three (on right) and one (on left) then right and left four with couple four (facing). Third: couple three take the lead and fourth: couple four. Fifth: the two head couples do the figure simultaneously ('two heads are better than one'). Sixth and last: it's the turn of the side couples.

I learned this dance from Jack Hamilton at Cecil Sharp House in May 1963 and was immediately struck first by the effectiveness of use of jigs rather than the usual reels and second by the fact that although, at times, the dance appears to be going across the phrase, provided the band stick rigidly to one 8 bar introduction and then the 32 bars, it all fits in very neatly. I also like the way it builds up into total activity. Eb is apparently short for Ebeneezer.

Blackberry quadrille

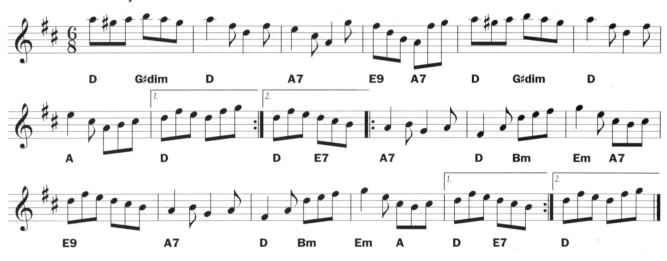

Farmers' jamboree

The Willow Tree

Eva Three step

Formation: couples in a circle facing counter-clockwise, man with his partner on his right.

Music: 32 bar 6/8 marches, steady tempo.

Step: walking step and pas-de-bas step.

A1 Man goes three steps to his left and claps while the woman does the same to her right (so they are apart).

Man and woman change places with three steps and clap. (Man goes behind woman).

Man and woman change places again with three steps and clap.

Man and woman then approach each other with two steps and take ballroom dance hold.

B1 Couples take two chassay steps counter-clockwise and two steps back.

Couples then dance round with a pas-de-bas step.

This dance has long been popular in the north of England and in Scotland since at least the end of the nineteenth century and has been printed in numerous old time ballroom dance books. It is referred to in a typical north east village dance of the 1940s mentioned in my book Discovering English Folk Dance, 3rd edition, page 65. The dance may be made progressive at the end of the A music with the man moving to the woman to his left. The crossing over in the A music can be embellished with single turns as desired.

The hills of Glenorchy

The Skye boat

Flint Street gallop

Formation: longways whole set for six couples.

Music: 48 bar double jigs.

Step: skipping or walking step.

A1 The top three men, holding hands, come up in a line and go down behind their three partners and back to place. At the same time the bottom three men do likewise round their partners but leading down and coming up behind their partners to place.

A2 The top three and bottom three women do the same round their men.

B1 Top two, middle two and bottom two couples do right and left hand stars.

B2 Top and bottom couples gallop through set and back, passing either over, under or round each other.

C1 The top and bottom couples *only* then cast out into the middle of the set. The whole set then faces up, double casts out left and back to place (in this way, the top and bottom couples progress into the middle of the set).

C2 Everybody swing.

I finalised this dance in October 1989 on the occasion of Inga Thoroughgood's (of Flint Street, Haddenham, Buckinghamshire) eighteenth birthday. The idea of the progression (C1) came from that well known Dutch dance Gort met Stroop (see The Willow Tree) and in the teaching of the dance this needs to be handled with care: warn the set to wait until the end couples are in the middle positions before they all face up and cast out.

Father Kelly's jig

Paddy O'Rafferty

The Willow Tree

Fred Pate

Formation: double Sicilian circle.

Music: 32 bar Scottish reels.

Step: walking step.

A1 *10 bars* Grand chain to original place: start by facing partners and imagine the two lines are in fact a circle of four couples and thus perform the grand chain all the way round to original place.

A2 *6 bars* All swing partners.

B1 All four ladies chain: all four women do a right hand star half-way round, the diagonally opposite men lead them out, turn them (as in ordinary ladies chain) and put them back into another right hand star to return to partner for final turn.

B2 Lines go forward and back and pass on to next line of four.

In July 1972 Dave Jones asked me to come and run a dance for local people and a visiting team of Swedish dancers at the Royal Oak, Ledbury, Herefordshire. The ballroom is long and narrow and the floor very springy. Tom Pate, I thought, would be a good dance but the gallop would present problems, so I started to alter the dance in my head and finished up with something which in fact bears little resemblance to the original. I later asked John Blomfield for a good title, explaining the circumstances of the dance's evolution and he instantly suggested the above title. 'Fred' was a well-known mythical radio comedy character of the 1960s.

Petronella

East Neuk of Fife

Haste to the wedding

Formation: longways duple proper.

Music: 32 bar double jigs.

Step: skipping step or walking step or skip change step.

A1 Second man leads the first woman down the set and back to place.

A2 The first man does the same with the second woman.

B1 The first couple circles left with the second woman (twice around) and 'pops' her through their arch towards the music (half progression).

B2 As **B1** but this time with the second man (progression complete).

The 'pop' is done as in the Dorset (Hardy MSS) version, that is on the first dotted note of bar 5 of the B music. My version is in fact based on the Dorset version and I first presented it at a Haddenham New Year's Extravaganza in 1988. I changed the first half of the original because I wanted something which was a bit of a teaser or a test for sobriety, as in any version of The Triumph. The method for the progression has always struck me as being ingenious.

Haste to the wedding

The ranting rake

The Willow Tree

Hornpipe promenade or progressive hornpipe

Formation: couples in a circle facing counter-clockwise. Man has his partner on his right.

Music: 16 bar hornpipes.

Step: single and double step as appropriate.

A1 Take partner with a promenade hold and move to the right with a step-close-step. Repeat to the left, then move forward with four walking steps. Repeat all the above.

B1 Hold partner with the right hand, advance with two single steps and retire with a step-close-step (almost passing right shoulders). Repeat holding left hands.
All swing partners with a two-hand cross-hand hold and a step-hop step. Men pass on to the woman in front (optional).

The origin of this dance is unknown. I learned it from the late Peter Dashwood but he told me he learned it elsewhere. I once saw a marvellous performance of this dance by a group of country dancers from Stockton-on-Tees in the drill hall at Sidmouth in the late sixties.

The Dancing Lesson

Katie Bairdie

Some say the devil's dead

The hotch-potch

Formation: large circle facing the centre, woman on the man's right.

Music: 32 bar jigs.

Step: walking step.

A1 All holding hands in a circle, move to the centre and out. Repeat.

A2 All face partner. The men will move clockwise

& around the circle and the women counter-clockwise

B1 as follows: all turn partner with the right hand a complete turn and men move on the inside of the circle to the next woman. All turn left hand a complete turn and men move on the outside to the next woman. All turn two hands a complete turn and men move on the inside to woman number four. All pass back to back or do-si-do. This is the new partner.

B2 Everybody swing, finish with woman on man's right facing the centre ready to start again.

This dance is based on an original idea by Bernard Chalk in the early 1970s but I have devised this version. The more discerning will recognise the opening moves of Virginia Reel done in a circle.

Out on the ocean

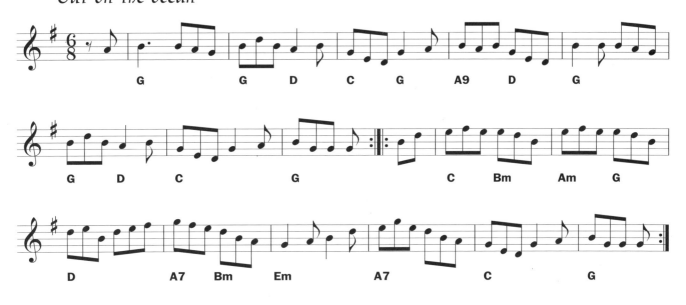

The humours of Glendart

The Willow Tree

The Itchington Long dance

Formation: longways duple proper.

Music: 32 bar double jigs.

Step: walking step or skip change step.

A1 Right and left hand star.

A2 Corners back-to-back, that is, the first man and the second woman pass back to back passing right shoulder and then second man and first woman do the same.

B1 First couple lead down the middle and back then cast one place (progression).

B2 Everybody swing.

There is not much to this dance; it is simply another longways dance but as such it is quite useful when one is looking for something which is not too difficult. I was dancing with Jenny Hill at the time and we virtually made it up as we went along. The occasion was a ceilidh at Long Itchington, Warwickshire in 1990. The reason for the title? If we have the Norfolk Long Dance then why not the Itchington Long Dance?

Fasten the leggin'

Sixpenny money

Jim's Reel

Formation: longways whole set for four couples.

Music: 48 bar single reels.

Step: walking step or skip change step as appropriate.

A1 Lines go forward and back, forward again and all turn partner's right hand one-and-a-half times around to finish on the opposite side.

A2 Repeat to places using left hands for the turn.

B1 First couple now perform 'the figure' by weaving

& down the set and back again as follows: first couple

B2 face each other, cross over, cast down behind second couple, face and cross again and cast behind third couple, cross again and cast down behind fourth couple and cross over at the bottom of the set, come **up** behind the fourth couple, cross again, come up behind the third couple and then pass through the second couple (woman first please) to finish in original place.

C1 All cast out singly, the men to the left, the women to the right, first couple make an arch at the bottom of the set, all come through and back to progressed place.

C2 Everybody swing partner.

I originally devised something like this as an up-to-date version of Lord of Carnarvon's Jig (Playford 1650) and first presented it at one of Brian Heaton's Chertsey dances in 1962 or 1963. I subsequently met other versions but this is the one I worked out on the (then) boring drive along the M1 to one of Jim Brannigan's ceilidhs at the 'Village Pump' in Coventry in 1970, hence the title.

The siege of Ennis

Johnny I do miss you

The Willow Tree

Lady Godiva's gallop

Formation: longways whole set for four couples.

Music: 48 bar polkas.

Step: walking step.

A1 Right and left hand turn partner.

A2 Two hand turn partner and back-to-back (do-si-do).

B1 Top and bottom couples gallop through the set and back, either under, over or round each other.

B2 Middle two couples circle left and right.

C1 Top two couples and bottom two couples star right and left.

C2 Top couple only 'piggy back' partner down the set, the man acting as the horse and the woman as the renowned lady, to the bottom of the set and everybody swing if there is time.

This dance was devised by myself in July 1976 and first presented at the Redcar Folk Festival of that year. This is a 'fun' dance and should be handled with some discretion, especially if the floor is slippery or partners are of unequal physique. Lady Godiva of course refers to the famous lady of Coventry riding on the horse's back in a tax protest but the historical reality is that she was stripped of her finery, not her clothes; a lady of rank never appeared in public in ordinary 'weeds'. In these days of so-called equality the rôle of the horse and the rider in this dance may of course be reversed but for this there is no historical precedent.

The Belfast polka

I have a bonnet

The Lancashire Reel

Formation: large circle, the men have their back to the centre facing their partner.

Music: 32 bar Irish polkas.

Step: walking step.

A1 All go back-to-back (do-si-do) with partner passing right shoulder. Then man turns the woman on the left with the left hand around.

A2 All go back-to-back with partner passing left shoulder. Then man turns the woman on the right with the right hand around and stay with each other (new partner).

B1 Balance and swing.

B2 All promenade counter-clockwise and finish as at the beginning (men with their back to the centre facing their new partner).

The origin of this dance seems to be unknown but it was printed in Northern Junket (October 1978) as an American circle dance. I learned it from John Chapman in 1979. It seems to be related to the Circle Mixer which I learned from Dick Witt in about 1965 but it is different in certain respects.

Girl with the blue dress on

The magic slipper

The Willow Tree

Marian's waltz

Formation: couples in a circle facing counter-clockwise.

Music: 32 bar waltzes.

Step: waltz step.

A1 Man and woman holding two hands, chassay four steps to the man's left and then balance to the man's right and left twice or single chassay right and left twice, almost on the spot.

A2 Repeat the other way to place.

B1 Partners holding right hands go forward and back and cross over with each other, man turning woman under his right arm.
Repeat to place.

B2 Waltz around (optional progression).

I learned this from John Chapman in 1976 who told me that it was a Welsh dance collected by the late Peggy Cash. I include it here because it is a very useful dance to teach people the basic feeling of the waltz rhythm before they launch into the much more difficult (for some) waltz around. In addition every dance programme should include something in waltz time.

Mary's waltz

Louis' waltz

Neil's Jig

Formation: Sicilian circle.

Music: 32 bar Scottish jigs.

Step: walking step.

A1 All pass back-to-back (do-si-do) with the opposite person. All turn partner with the right hand a complete turn.

A2 The two men turn each other with the left hand a complete turn and then, still keeping hold, pick up their partner round the waist and turn again. Break the hold in the middle and go into…

B1 …a whole ladies chain.

B2 Couples advance and retire and pass onto the next couple round the room.

I learned this from the late Brian Conner at Rayleigh in Essex in the summer of 1959 and for a long time I thought it was his dance. Subsequently I discovered that it was devised by a Neil Bawden of Bebbington in the Wirral, Cheshire.

Frontispiece from Henry Playford's The Dancing Master, first volume, 18th edition.

Major Mackie's

Bonnie Dundee

The Willow Tree

Putney Bridge

Formation: longways duple improper.

Music: 16 bar schottisches.

Step: single and double step.

A1 *4 bars* First man swings second woman with right arm hold twice around while second man does the same with the first woman (first man goes first).

4 bars First man swings his own partner twice around with a left arm hold while the second man does the same with his partner (first man goes first).

B1 *4 bars* First couple does two chassay steps down the middle and back to place while the second couple (separated) does two chassay steps up the outside and back to place. First couple then cast out to progressed place.

4 bars Everybody swing with a two-hand cross-hand hold.

This dance happened by chance one night in the early sixties in Wallington, Surrey. It was published in English Dance and Song volume XXXII number 2, summer 1970. Putney Bridge is where I was living at the time and John Kirkpatrick lived just round the corner, up the reach as it were. He wrote the tunes given here, Putney Reach and Charabanc schottische. The dance is really a version of Nottingham Swing and is quite exhausting if allowed to go on too long.

Putney Reach © *John Kirkpatrick*

Charabanc schottische © *John Kirkpatrick*

Soldiers' Joy

Formation: medium-sized circle facing the centre, woman on man's right.

Music: 32 bar rants.

Step: walking step or rant or polka step if possible.

A1 All women, moving in one step join hands and circle to the left and right back to place, stepping if possible.

A2 The men do the same but they circle right then left to finish facing their partner with their back to the centre.

B1 All left-hand turn partner a complete turn and then the person to their right (neighbour) a complete right-hand turn. All turn partner left again and then take neighbour as the new partner. Put the woman on the man's right.

B2 All promenade counter-clockwise and at the end gently guide the women in for their next circle left.

I learned this from Sue Burnett at the National Folk Music Festival, Sutton Bonnington, Nottinghamshire in 1984. In the original Irish version (see O'Rafferty, Irish Folk Dances Book 1, 1934) the men circle left. The dance only works with medium sized circles when it can be very effective provided people remember the difference between left and right and remember to join the circle in time. The stepping calls for concentrated team work.

Far from home

Pigtown Fling

The Willow Tree

Tavistock hornpipe

Formation: longways duple proper.

Music: 32 bar hornpipes.

Step: single and double step.

A1 All arm right with partner twice around and then arm left twice around.

A2 First couple link arms between second couple facing down the room in a line of four. Move down the room in this line, turn individually, link up again and move back up. On the way up bring the twos up one place into a circle of four (progression).

B1 Circle to the left and right.

B2 Couples dance around each other using the cross-hand hold or a ballroom dance hold.

This dance emerged in January 1971 and was first performed at a dance in Tavistock Town Hall. It is really a version of the Surrey dance Tink-a-Tink, the difference being that all dancers are active in the version here. I was told afterwards that Angela Rippon, the BBC personality, was in the hall that night, so that made two of us: she was president of the Devon District of the EFDSS and I was president of Coventry District.

The honeysuckle

The Galway

The willow tree

Formation: longways whole set for eight couples.

Music: 48 bar double jigs.

Step: walking step.

A1 First couple gallop down the set, man change partners with the bottom man and gallop back with the new woman to the top.

A2 Bottom man does the same retrieving his partner.

B1 Top and bottom couples strip the willow simultaneously until they meet each other in the middle of the set where they make…

B2 …a four-handed arch (the rest of the set must make room for them).

C1 The rest of the set cast out, up or down, to the left or right, pass in through the side arches and lead back through the top or bottom arch to place (progression).

C2 Everybody swing.

The idea for this dance came from the Dutch dance, Gort met Stroop (Porridge with Syrup) but I could not quite get it right. Rory McEwan once saw my rough diagrams and thought I was planning a battle. Eventually I got it the way I wanted and I first presented it on a Thursday night in Cecil Sharp House on January 11th 1968. Apparently there was an American lady there that night and she flew back home the next day and presented it on that evening at the country dance club in Cambridge, Massachusets. The dance was subsequently published in English Dance and Song volume XXX number 3 (Autumn 1968). Since then the dance seems to have achieved international notoriety with variations of course. The inspiration for the title came from the stripping of the willow and a beautiful willow tree I used to know on a tributary of the River Ouse at the Black Bridge, Hemingford Abbots in what was then Huntingdonshire.

Dusty windowsills

The Willow Tree

WRING OUT THE DISHRAG

Formation: Sicilian circle.

Music: 32 bar Kerry polkas getting imperceptibly faster.

Note: The basic rule is that no one is allowed to let go until the last eight bars.

Step: walking step.

A1 Circle left and right with facing couple.

A2 Clockwise couple duck half-way under the opposite arch and back. Counter-clockwise couple do the same.

B1 The clockwise couple dive right through the opposite arch and come back to place. (The diving couple should push their joined hands up as they go through, turn away from each other and then bring the resulting arch over the other couple. The other couple should follow the movement naturally and not turn under their own arch until the last moment. There is no need to duck). This is now repeated by the other couple.

B2 Breaking the circle, couples advance and retire and pass onto the next couple round the room, hoping they have learned the same version, or swing partners and progress.

I learned this dance from Ron Smedley at a dance in Derby in 1958. When running an evening's dance I usually leave this one towards the end as my 'novelty number'. It is very good for loosening up frozen joints if done properly. When I did it in Holland they translated it as 'De Dweil/Vaatdoek Uitwringen'. Those who practise long-sword dancing should have no problems with B1.

Peg Ryan's

Johnny Mickey Barry's